First published in the UK in 2019 by Studio Press Books,
part of Bonnier Books UK,
The Plaza, 535 King's Road,
London, SW10 0SZ

studiopressbooks.co.uk
bonnierbooks.co.uk

Printed in Poland
1 3 5 7 9 10 8 6 4 2

ISBN 978-1-78741-526-3

Written by Frankie Jones
Designed by Wendy Bartlet
Cover designed by Rob Ward
Additional illustrations by Emily McGorman-Bruce and Nigel Parkinson

BEANO HOW TO MAKE A COMIC

CONTENTS

STORY AND PLOT

CREATE YOUR OWN COMIC

RESOURCES

Why I Love Comics

Drawing comics is fun! There, the secret is out! It can be long hours and hard work, but it's fun!

I started drawing when I was under two years old. And I've never stopped. If it wasn't fun, would I do that?

Telling a story in pictures isn't the same as telling a story just in words. The pictures should tell the story in a clear, funny, exciting way and the words should add detail, giving extra depth and humour.

There aren't very many rules in making comics. Action should always come from the left, and you read a strip from the left and then down the page. Otherwise, anything goes!

Drawing Dennis and Gnasher is great. They only do things that are heroic, wild, funny, extreme or exciting. So, when they run, it's wild or exciting. When they stand still, it's heroic. When they're sad, it's extreme.

When you create your own comic, your characters can say anything you want, go anywhere, do anything. There are lots of ideas and tips in this book, but feel free to experiment and make up your own characters and stories! Whatever you choose to do, make it heroic, exciting and extreme. And above all, have fun!

Nigel Parkinson
Illustrator of Dennis, Gnasher, Minnie the Minx, The Bash Street Kids, Bananaman, Roger the Dodger and many more!

NIGEL
PARKINSON.

6

WHY I LOVE COMICS

MY LOVE OF BOOKS STARTED BEFORE I COULD EVEN READ. AFTER DISCOVERING PICTURE BOOKS, IT WASN'T LONG BEFORE I MADE THE MOVE INTO COMICS. I GREW UP READING GARFIELD, ORSON'S FARM AND OF COURSE BEANO AND DANDY! THAT'S WHEN MY LOVE OF COMICS BEGAN AND IT'S SOMETHING I'VE NEVER GROWN OUT OF!

I HAD ALWAYS LOVED DRAWING, AND READING COMICS INSPIRED ME TO MAKE MY OWN. I WOULD DREAM UP ADVENTURES FOR MY FAVOURITE CHARACTERS FROM BOOKS, TV SHOWS OR COMICS AND FILL SKETCH BOOKS WITH LITTLE SKITS!

IT'S GREAT FUN TO THINK OF YOUR OWN STORIES FOR YOUR FAVOURITE CHARACTERS, AND EVERYONE SHOULD BE ENCOURAGED TO TRY MAKING COMICS THEMSELVES - THIS BOOK IS THE PERFECT PLACE TO START.

FOLLOW THE STEP-BY-STEPS TO LEARN HOW TO DRAW DENNIS, MINNIE, GNASHER, JJ AND ROGER AND THEN HAVE A LOOK AT THE STORY IDEAS TO HELP YOU CREATE YOUR VERY OWN ADVENTURES.

WHEN YOU READ A BOOK, PEOPLE HAVE THEIR OWN INTERPRETATIONS OF HOW THE SCENES LOOK. WITH A COMIC, YOU CAN CONVEY EXACTLY WHAT YOU WANT PEOPLE TO SEE, SO THEY ARE SHARING IN YOUR IMAGINATION! WHAT COULD BE BETTER THAN THAT?

EMILY MCGORMAN-BRUCE ILLUSTRATOR OF RUBI'S SCREWTOP SCIENCE, PAUL THE POTATO AND PIE FACE.

HOW TO USE THIS BOOK

Beano has been around **FOREVER**.
Well, almost. It's been around for over eighty years —
which makes it as old as great-auntie Doris. Over the
eight decades, your favourite comic has been created by
LOADS of illustrators, comic book artists and writers —
and now it's your turn to join the ranks of these wonderful
people who might just have the best job in the world.

This book is filled with everything you need to know to start
drawing, writing and making your own comic strips. You'll find
information on what a comic is, step-by-steps on drawing the
most popular Beano characters and how to come up with story
ideas (plus you get to create your own Menace character!).
There's also space to draw your own
comic strips, and there are lots of
Beano characters and drawings
for you to copy and use in
your own creations.

So, what are you waiting for?
Sharpen your pencil and start doodling!

Things You'll Need

Pencils

A pencil sharpener

An eraser

Felt-tip pens
(It's useful to have black pens
in a range of thicknesses)

Spare paper, or a sketchbook

A stack of Beano comics

A 6-sided dice

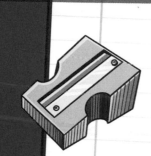

BEANO

WHAT IS A COMIC?

If you want to know what a comic is, ~~have you been living under a rock?~~ you're in the right place!

A comic is a (usually funny) story told through a series of panels, which contain drawings and words. A comic strip is the sequence of drawings that tell the story, and these often appear in collections in comic books.

Beano is one of the most famous comic books for kids, and has been going for over eighty years. Some of the most recognisable comic book characters come from Beano including Dennis, Minnie the Minx, Bananaman, Billy Whizz and original cover star Big Eggo.

A COMIC STRIP IS MADE UP OF PANELS...

It takes a whole team of people to make a comic like Beano.

A WRITER COMES UP WITH THE STORYLINES FOR THE COMIC, AND PLANS WHAT WILL HAPPEN IN EACH PANEL OF THE STRIP.

A COMIC BOOK ARTIST DRAWS THE PICTURES, BASED ON THE WRITER'S STORYLINE. SOMETIMES THE WRITER AND ARTIST ARE THE SAME (VERY TALENTED) PERSON.

A COLOURIST ADDS COLOUR TO THE PICTURES. YES – YOU CAN GET A JOB COLOURING IN!

AN EDITOR MAKES SURE EVERYTHING IS SPELT CORRECTLY AND PUTS THE COMIC BOOK TOGETHER. SOMETIMES THE EDITOR WILL CHIP IN TO THE COMIC STRIP WITH THEIR OWN COMMENTS!

But this book puts you in charge. You are the writer, artist, colourist and editor – all rolled into one!

PENCIL, INK AND COLOUR

All comic artists work in different ways, using a range of materials and tools. Whatever their method, they all agree on one thing: you've got to do things in the right order to make sure your finished drawing has no mistakes and doesn't get smudged!

Here's the best way to plan, outline and finish your drawing:

PENCIL – Plan your drawing in pencil. You can add in guidelines, erase any mistakes and make sure the drawing is perfect before you add ink or felt tip. Make sure to use a light line, so you can erase any marks after inking.

INK – Start by inking the outline and details of your character in black. We recommend using black felt tip pens. You can use different thicknesses of pen, depending on the line you are drawing.

DRY – Let your outline dry, to avoid any smudging.

BLACK – Using your black felt tips, colour in any black details, such as the stripes on Dennis's jumper. Again, let this dry before moving on to the next step.

COLOUR – Add one colour at a time, making sure to colour in as neatly as possible! Let each colour dry before adding the next.

Dennis has been drawn here in a very light pencil.
Use your black felt tip pens to ink the outline and
fill in the black areas, and then add colour!

HOW TO DRAW DENNIS

Nigel illustrates Dennis every week! Follow the step-by-steps below to draw Beano's iconic character.

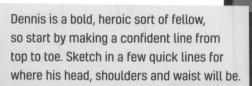

Dennis is a bold, heroic sort of fellow, so start by making a confident line from top to toe. Sketch in a few quick lines for where his head, shoulders and waist will be.

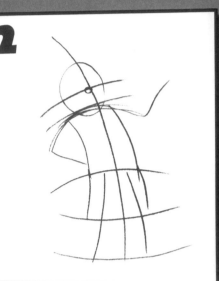

On the centre line, where the head will be draw in the nose. Everything is easier to fit in if you've decided where the nose will be. Add in a rough line for the arms and legs.

Start to fill in the shapes for the arms, hands, torso, legs and feet. Sketch in where the eyes will go.

EXPERT TIP

DENNIS IS ALWAYS DYNAMIC. HE'S ALWAYS ON THE MOVE, LEANING IN OR LEANING BACK. MAKE SURE HIS POSTURE REFLECTS THIS!

4

Add a bit more detail to Dennis's body and, most importantly, decide on the expression he is pulling!

5

Fill in details like ears, stripes, socks and finally hair – go wild and enjoy adding that hair!

6

Rub out the construction lines and there's Dennis! You just need to add colour to finish off.

NOT BAD!

DENNIS'S
POSES AND EXPRESSIONS

Dennis gets up to plenty of mischief, so you'll need to be able to draw him in different poses and making different faces. Here are some ideas for you to use in your comic strips! Practise drawing your favourite poses and expressions on a spare sheet of paper.

Practise drawing Dennis and add him to this comic strip.
Fill in the speech bubbles with hilarious dialogue.

EXPERT TIP

PLAN YOUR STRIP ON A
PIECE OF PAPER BEFORE
DRAWING IT IN HERE.
REMEMBER TO USE A PENCIL FIRST!

HOW TO DRAW GNASHER

Gnasher is Dennis's faithful sidekick, and is never far from his friend. Check out Nigel's step-by-step instructions for drawing this Abyssinian wire-haired tripe hound.

1

Start by drawing your guideline. Just like Dennis, Gnasher is always on the move, so curve the line backwards. Add in some rough lines to show where the eyes, head and legs will go.

2

Add in a circle for the head and body, as well as four lines for the arms and legs.

3

Start to fill in some rough shapes: Gnasher's upturned snout, his ears, eyes, arms and legs.

GNASH GNASH!

4

Add some more details like
Gnasher's toothy grin and his paws.

5

Fur is the last thing to add
– go wild!

6

Rub out the construction
lines and then add colour!

EXPERT TIP

GNASHER IS THE DOG
VERSION OF DENNIS:
STURDY, BRAVE AND ALWAYS
CHEERFUL. TRY TO REFLECT
THIS IN YOUR DRAWINGS.

GNASHER'S POSES AND EXPRESSIONS

Here are some Gnasher poses and expressions for you to copy.

Practise drawing Gnasher by adding him to this comic strip and filling in the speech bubbles.

HOW TO DRAW MINNIE

Minnie is always getting up to mischief and is a great character to draw! Follow Emily's step-by-step instructions and try your hand at drawing this Minx.

1

Rough out a pose with some basic shapes – press lightly here as you'll want to rub out these lines later. Put a cross on the face to show the direction she's going to be looking.

2

Using your rough sketch as a base, draw the shape of her face – placing her nose in the middle. Draw in her beret, pigtails, hands and add the cuffs of her clothes.

3

Add detail to the hair, leaving a few bits out of place at the bottom and add ribbons. Draw in her clothes and don't forget the pom-pom on her beret!

EXPERT TIP

MINNIE IS MISCHIEVOUS – MAKE SURE SHE HAS A GOOD GRIN!

4

Draw in her hands using the guidelines you made earlier and don't forget her shoes. Now is a good time to draw her legs too – including those knobbly knees!

5

It's time for the face. Draw the eyes touching the circle you made for the nose. Add in a big smile to show she's up to something! Draw in the stripes for the jumper, too.

6

Make the smile into a toothy grin. Now she really looks like she's up to something! Go over everything in pen and colour in the black areas.

7

Erase your pencil lines underneath the pen (make sure the pen is dry first) and now you're ready to add colour!

MINNIE'S
POSES AND EXPRESSIONS

Copy and use these Minnie poses in your next Minx-ing comic.

Add Minnie into this comic strip with sporty JJ and fill in the bubbles with your own dialogue.

HOW TO DRAW ROGER

Roger always has a trick up his sleeve, and so does Emily, the Beano illustrator. Follow her instructions and have a go!

1

Rough out a pose using basic shapes. You'll rub these out later. Put a cross on the head to show where he's looking. Roger has one hand behind his back because he's probably hiding something!

2

Draw the outline of Roger's face and add a circle for his nose on the middle line. Draw in the hands, and add in his cuffs and collars.

3

Draw in Roger's hair line, his jumper and trousers.

4

Now it's time to add his fingers. He's got a reassuring thumb pointing towards him as if to say "I've got this!". It's also time to draw in his shoes.

26

5

Add in a confident smile showing his top row of teeth. Draw his eyes touching his nose and don't forget his eyebrows! For the shirt, start by drawing in stripes.

6

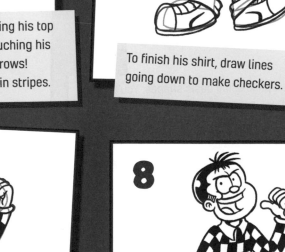

To finish his shirt, draw lines going down to make checkers.

7

Draw in Roger's fringe and add the highlight to the back of his head. Now it's time to go over the pencil in pen. Fill in the squares on his shirt, his trousers and hair.

8

Erase your pencil lines underneath the pen (make sure the pen is dry first) and now you're ready to add colours!

ROGER'S POSES AND EXPRESSIONS

Here are some of Roger's best dodges. Practise drawing these poses and add them to your own strips!

Practise drawing Roger and add him to this comic strip. Add your own hilarious dialogue to the bubbles.

29

HOW TO DRAW JJ

JJ is a great character to add into your comics for a bit of action. Emily is here to give you the step-by-steps you need to follow to draw JJ!

Rough out a pose with basic shapes - keeping in mind that JJ loves to run! Put a cross on the circle to show the direction she's looking.

Using the rough shapes, draw in the outline of JJ's face, add the shape of her hair and rough out the hand shapes too. Pop her nose on the middle line on her face.

Add detail to her hair, and draw in her top, trousers and arms. We'll also draw in her hands at this stage.

4

Add the stripes to her top and draw her running shoes in so she's not running in bare feet!

5

Draw in her eyes touching her nose and give her a big happy smile – she's at her happiest when she's running! Now would be a good time to draw over your sketch in pen too!

6

Erase your pencil lines underneath the pen (make sure the pen is dry first). Now you're ready to add colours!

EXPERT TIP

JJ IS VERY ACTIVE, THINK ABOUT THIS WHEN DECIDING HER POSE.

JJ'S
POSES AND EXPRESSIONS

JJ is always on the move, so you'll need to practise drawing her in different action poses. Here are some poses to try!

Practise drawing JJ and add her to this comic strip.
Don't forget to add some dialogue!

CREATE A CHARACTER

Have you ever wished you could appear in Beano? Here's your chance! Answer this questionnaire to decide what your character will be like, and then turn the page to design your character.

MENACE NAME: ....

(TO COME UP WITH YOUR MENACE NAME, THINK OF A WORD THAT STARTS WITH THE SAME LETTER AS YOUR FIRST NAME BUT ALSO DESCRIBES YOUR CHARACTER OR SPECIAL POWER. FOR EXAMPLE YOU COULD BE JUMPING JAMAL OR MEG THE MAGICIAN!)

AGE: ....

SUPER POWER OR TALENT: ....

CATCHPHRASE: ....

DISTINGUISHING FEATURE: ....

BEST FRIENDS: (TICK THE BOXES BELOW)

PET: ....

LIKES: ....

DISLIKES: ....

WANT TO MAKE MORE CHARACTERS? WHY NOT USE THIS QUESTIONNAIRE TO MAKE YOUR FRIENDS AND FAMILY INTO COMIC STARS?

FAVOURITE PLACE
IN BEANOTOWN: ....

PROUDEST MOMENT: ....

....

MOST EMBARRASSING
MOMENT: ....

....

FAVOURITE PRANKING DEVICE: (TICK THE BOXES BELOW)

FAVOURITE OUTFIT: ....

Now you know almost everything about your new star character, it's time to bring them to life. Draw a body outline below, and then sketch some details.

COMIC CHARACTERS ARE EXAGGERATED, SO WHY NOT GIVE YOUR CHARACTER A BIG HAIRSTYLE?

THINK ABOUT HOW YOUR CHARACTER IS FEELING, AND SHOW THIS ON THEIR FACE.

IS YOUR CHARACTER HOLDING ANYTHING? PERHAPS THEY'VE GOT A PRANKING DEVICE READY!

DRESS YOUR CHARACTER IN THEIR FAVOURITE OUTFIT. IT'S A GOOD IDEA TO PICK A SIMPLE DESIGN, AS YOU DON'T WANT TO HAVE TO REDRAW SOMETHING COMPLICATED EIGHT TIMES ON A PAGE!

EXPERT TIP

IF YOU WANT TO DRAW A POSE, ASK A FRIEND TO STRIKE THAT POSE AND THEN MAKE A QUICK SKETCH OF THE SHAPE THEIR BODY MAKES.

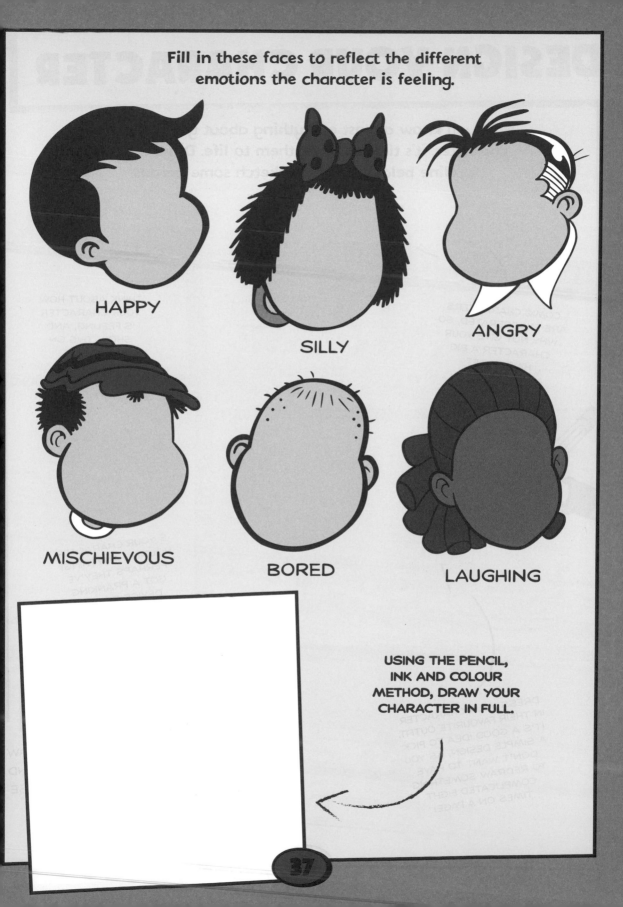

Fill in these faces to reflect the different emotions the character is feeling.

HAPPY

SILLY

ANGRY

MISCHIEVOUS

BORED

LAUGHING

USING THE PENCIL, INK AND COLOUR METHOD, DRAW YOUR CHARACTER IN FULL.

It's time for your character to make their Beano debut — add them into the scenes below and write some dialogue to complete the story.

HOW TO DRAW PROPS

You're now pretty good at drawing comic book characters (unless you skipped the last 39 pages!) so it's time to practise drawing props! Props are objects that characters use, like skateboards that whizz them around and squishy tomatoes that they use in pranks.

Here are some Beano-riffic props for you to use in your comic strips. Try copying them in the boxes below.

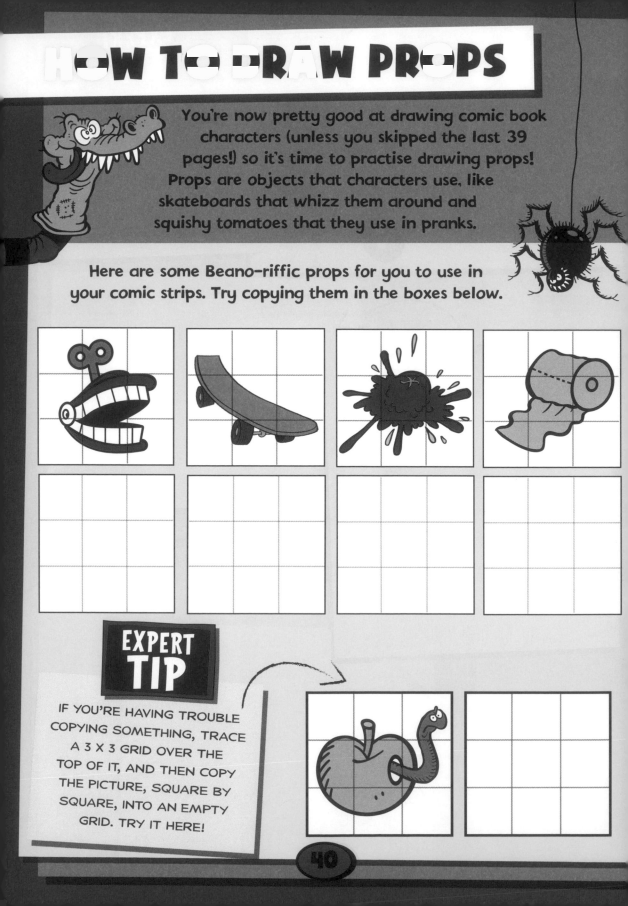

EXPERT TIP

IF YOU'RE HAVING TROUBLE COPYING SOMETHING, TRACE A 3 X 3 GRID OVER THE TOP OF IT, AND THEN COPY THE PICTURE, SQUARE BY SQUARE, INTO AN EMPTY GRID. TRY IT HERE!

EXPERT TIP

DO YOU WANT TO ADD A PROP THAT'S NOT IN THIS BOOK? FIND THE OBJECT (OR A PICTURE OF IT) TO COPY AND DRAW IT IN PENCIL FIRST. IF IT'S COMPLICATED, TRY BREAKING IT DOWN INTO SHAPES FIRST, AND THEN ADD THE DETAIL.

DESIGN A SUPER-FAST SCOOTER.

CREATE A BRAND-NEW PRANK DEVICE.

DRAW A SANDWICH FOR A MENACE.

HOW TO DRAW BACKGROUNDS

You can't have all the amazing characters, action and props on a white background (unless your story takes place in a white void of nothingness), so you'll need to add backgrounds.

A background is used to set the scene. It helps the reader work out where the story is taking place (is it inside, outside, on the moon, underground?) and when the action is happening (is it night, day, winter, summer?).

Sometimes the background will show a specific location (like Bash Street School or Dennis's house) and sometimes it will just show a generic scene (trees and a blue sky instantly tell the reader the character is outside on a sunny day!).

The background you use will depend on a few things:

WHERE the story is taking place (obviously!)

THE SIZE of the panel you are drawing in (you can show more in a wide panel)

THE VIEW OF THE ACTION - is it a close up on the character's face, or is it a wider shot showing more of their body and more background?

EXPERT TIP

IF YOU ARE CREATING YOUR OWN COMIC BOOK WORLD YOU COULD PUT TOGETHER A MOOD BOARD OF REAL-LIFE BUILDINGS AND LOCATIONS THAT INSPIRE YOU.

Here are some Beano backgrounds for you to use and copy.

Try drawing your favourite Beanotown location here, behind the characters.

ADD BACKGROUNDS TO THESE COMIC STRIPS

Decide where the action in these comic strips is taking place, and add the background details. Remember to decide if the panel is showing a close-up or zoomed-out scene. When you're done, add some funny dialogue.

HOW TO DRAW
SOUND EFFECTS

You might think that sound effects (or **SFX**) are reserved for blockbuster movies and **TV** dramas, but you can totally have sound in your comics. They're not sounds you can hear, but you can make the reader imagine what the comic sounds like, just by using a word, an interesting shape, a cool font and bright colours. Sound effects can add humour, build tension and even provide action. You can add **SFX** to your comic strips, either within panels – or even taking up a whole panel (if it's a really, really, really, REALLY loud noise).

SHAPE – Think about the shape you want to put your sound effect in. Is the noise jagged and sharp, soft and fluffy or gloopy and runny? By placing the SFX into a shape, you can give the reader an idea of what sound they should imagine.

FONT – The font type and size can really help the reader to 'hear' the sound. Should the word be in capitals, or all lower case? Should the letters be crowded together, or spaced out? Try whispering, saying or shouting the noise, and imagine what it could look like written down.

WORD – The word you choose for your sound effect should be onomatopoeic (that means it sounds like the sound). There are some amazing onomatopoeic words that already exist like

BOOM! FIZZLE SPLAT! ROAR! and CRUNCH!

POP!

If a word doesn't exist for the sound, you can make one up. Simply listen to the sound, or try to make it yourself, and think about which letters you could use to make the noise.

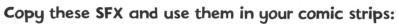

Copy these SFX and use them in your comic strips:

KA-BOOM!

WOOF!

SPLASH!

WHIZZ!

CRASH!

Try creating your own SFX bursts for these noises.
You might have to invent a new word:

HEAVY RAIN

THE LOUDEST
BELCH EVER

ESCAPING GAS

A SPOOKY GHOST

AN ANGRY SEAGULL

ADD SOUND EFFECTS TO THESE COMIC STRIPS

Look at what's happening in these comic strips, and add your own SFX bursts and bubbles to help the reader 'hear' all the noises! Finish off by adding in some dialogue.

CAPTIONS AND BUBBLES

It is true; a picture speaks a thousand words, but ACTUAL words are useful to help move the plot along. In comics, you can include text in caption boxes, in dialogue (speech bubbles) and in thought bubbles.

A CAPTION BOX IS THAT LITTLE BOX AT THE TOP (OR SOMETIMES BOTTOM) OF A PANEL. IT DOESN'T INCLUDE DIALOGUE, BUT IS INSTEAD THE VOICE OF THE AUTHOR – AND SOMETIMES EDITOR. IT'S USED TO SET UP THE SCENE AT THE BEGINNING OF A STRIP OR TO EXPLAIN THE STORY IN MORE DETAIL. IT'S ALSO USED TO SHOW A CHANGE IN TIME OR LOCATION.

ADD DRAWINGS TO THE STRIP BELOW TO SEE HOW THE CAPTION BOXES WORK.

CAPTION BOXES

THE STORY IS SET UP HERE.

THIS CAPTION TELLS US THAT TIME HAS MOVED ON.

MINNIE HAS WOKEN UP, FEELING MISCHIEVOUS...

LATER THAT DAY...

TEE-HEE-HEE! I HAVE A PLAN!

OUCH THAT LOOKS LIKE IT HURT! – ED

SOMETIMES THE EDITOR ADDS A FUNNY COMMENT IN A CAPTION BOX.

SPEECH BUBBLES

A lot of the story in a comic strip is shown through what the characters say – in other words, the dialogue. This is shown through speech bubbles.

WHEN YOU WRITE SPEECH, TRY TO MAKE IT SOUND NATURAL - AND THINK ABOUT WHETHER THE CHARACTER SPEAKS IN A CERTAIN WAY. YOU COULD TEST THIS OUT BY SPEAKING THE LINES OUT LOUD, IN THAT CHARACTER'S VOICE.

IF YOUR CHARACTER HAS A LOT TO SAY,

YOU CAN SPLIT THE BUBBLES LIKE THIS.

LIKE SFX, YOU CAN SHOW IF SOMEONE IS SHOUTING BY USING A SPIKY BUBBLE...

... OR SHOW SOMEONE IS WHISPERING WITH A DOTTED BUBBLE.

THIS IS A STANDARD SPEECH BUBBLE, THE STEM SHOULD POINT TOWARDS THE CHARACTER'S MOUTH.

THOUGHT BUBBLES

Characters don't always speak their minds; sometimes they can let the readers know their secrets through thought bubbles!

THOUGHT BUBBLES CAN BE USED TO:

• SHOW WHAT ANIMAL CHARACTERS (THAT DON'T TALK) ARE THINKING

• SHOW WHAT A CHARACTER REALLY THINKS (THIS IS OFTEN DIFFERENT TO WHAT THEY'RE SAYING)

• SHOW WHAT A CHARACTER IS DREAMING ABOUT - USUALLY A DREAM BUBBLE WILL CONTAIN PICTURES RATHER THAN WORDS

• TELL A CHARACTER'S SECRET PLAN

Write or draw in what these characters are thinking about:

ADD CAPTIONS AND BUBBLES TO THIS COMIC STRIP

Complete this comic strip, adding in caption boxes, speech bubbles, thought bubbles and – of course – the words to go with them!

54

55

You may have heard people say "don't judge a book by its cover", but the truth is, we all do. Look at the cover for this book. It's awesome, right? It makes you want to open it up and start creating your own comic. You want the cover of your comic to grab the reader's attention, and to give them a teaser of what's inside. Just take a look at your favourite Beano covers for inspiration.

THIS COULD BE SOMETHING SEASONAL OR SOMETHING INCLUDED IN THE COMIC, LIKE A FEATURE OR A COMPETITION!

ADD A SUPER-FUN CAPTION HERE!

BEANO

YOU COULD A
THE TITLE OF
MOST EXCIT
STRIP HERE
ADD A PHRA
THAT SUMS
THE THEME
THE COMIC. (
BRIGHT, BO
LETTERING T
STANDS OU

INTERESTING AND EPIC COMIC TITLE

YOU CAN ADD IN EXTRA BOXES OR PANELS THAT SHOW WHAT ELSE IS INCLUDED IN THE COMIC BOOK.

PLUS! What else is in your comic?

PLUS! Are there puzzles, games or pranks?

PLUS! Who else features in your comic strips?

HAVE A GO AT COMPLETING YOUR OWN BEANO COVER ON THE NEXT PAGE!

CREATING STORIES

So you can draw all your favourite characters with props, backgrounds, SFX and speech bubbles. That's great, but only if you have a story for them to tell!

You might have lots of ideas for storylines or you might need some help in thinking up an awesome story (don't worry, there are plenty of ideas and prompts on the next few pages!). Once you have an idea, you'll need to work out the plot.

All stories have a **BEGINNING**, **MIDDLE** and **END**. What happens at each point is up to you. Below are some pointers.

At the **BEGINNING** of your story you should introduce the main character and set the scene.

The **MIDDLE** of the story is where the action happens — introduce a problem for your character to overcome.

The **END** of the story should wrap everything up nicely. The problem should be fixed — and you can decide if the story has a happy or sad ending.

DONT FORGET TO HAVE FUN AND MAKE YOUR STORY AS BANANAS AS YOU LIKE — JUST LIKE ME!

STORY SHEET

Try filling in this story sheet, to help you plan
[wh]at happens in your strip. There are more of these at
[the] back of the book, so you can plan even more stories!

SOMETIMES IT'S EASIER TO COME UP WITH A TITLE **AFTER** YOU'VE WORKED OUT THE PLOT.

TITLE

BEGINNING

WHO IS THE MAIN CHARACTER IN THE STORY? ---------------------------------

WHAT DOES THE CHARACTER WANT OR NEED? ----------------------------------

----

WHERE IS THE STORY SET? -----------------------------------

MIDDLE

WHAT PROBLEM DOES YOUR CHARACTER COME UP AGAINST?

WORKING OUT WHAT YOUR CHARACTER **WANTS** OR **NEEDS** IS A GOOD WAY TO FIND A PROBLEM FOR THE MIDDLE. PERHAPS THEY CAN'T GET WHAT THEY WANT.

HOW DOES YOUR CHARACTER REACT TO THE PROBLEM?

HOW DOES THE CHARACTER FEEL? ---

WHAT'S THE MAIN ACTION? -----------------------------------

END

HOW IS THE PROBLEM SOLVED? --------------------------------

YOU CAN ALWAYS LEAVE YOUR STORY ON A CLIFFHANGER AND CONTINUE IT IN ANOTHER STRIP!

HOW DOES YOUR CHARACTER FEEL? -----------------------------------

----

59

ROLL A STORY

Stuck for ideas?
Just grab a dice and get inspired!
Roll the dice once for each category to come
up with a Beano-riffic storyline. You must include
everything you rolled in your new comic strip!

ROLL 1

CHOOSE A MAIN CHARACTER

1: DENNIS
2: GNASHER
3: MINNIE
4: ROGER
5: WALTER
6: TRICKY DICKY

ROLL 2

CHOOSE A SECOND CHARACTER

1: GNIPPER
2: TOOTS
3: BANANAMAN
4: JJ
5: BEA
6: BILLY WHIZZ

ROLL 3

CHOOSE A LOCATION

1: BASH STREET SCHOOL
2: HORRIBLE HALL
3: BEANOTOWN MUSEUM
4: DUCK ISLAND
5: YOUR HOUSE
6: THE MOON

ROLL 4

CHOOSE AN EVENT

1: A BIRTHDAY PARTY
2: FIRST DAY OF SCHOOL
3: SKATEBOARDING
COMPETITION
4: CHRISTMAS DAY
5: LAST DAY OF SCHOOL
6: DENTIST APPOINTMENT

WRITE WHAT YOU ROLLED HERE, AND THEN FILL IN A BLANK STORY SHEET WITH YOUR IDEAS! YOU CAN COME BACK TO THIS PAGE – THE COMBINATIONS ARE ALMOST* UNLIMITED!

MAIN CHARACTER ----------------------------

SECONDARY CHARACTER ----------------------

LOCATION --------------------------------------

EVENT --

OBJECT --

WORD --

ROLL 5

CHOOSE AN OBJECT

1: STINK BOMB
2: GO-KART
3: SAUSAGES
4: WHOOPEE CUSHION
5: FOOTBALL
6: SKATEBOARD

MAIN CHARACTER ----------------------------

SECONDARY CHARACTER ----------------------

LOCATION --------------------------------------

EVENT --

OBJECT --

WORD --

ROLL 6

CHOOSE A WORD

1: BEANO-RIFFIC
2: AWESOME
3: UNICORN
4: HOMEWORK
5: NAPPY
6: DINOSAUR

MAIN CHARACTER ----------------------------

SECONDARY CHARACTER ----------------------

LOCATION --------------------------------------

EVENT --

OBJECT --

WORD --

*ACTUALLY, THERE ARE 46,656 POSSIBLE COMBINATIONS – THAT'S A LOT OF COMIC STRIPS TO WRITE!

MAIN CHARACTER ----------------------------

SECONDARY CHARACTER ----------------------

LOCATION --------------------------------------

EVENT --

OBJECT --

WORD --

61

THE COMIC CHALLENGE

Don't have a dice to roll a story? Never fear! The Beano Comic Challenge is here! For a quick comic challenge, you must include the following characters, locations, objects and words. Draw your comic in the empty panels below!

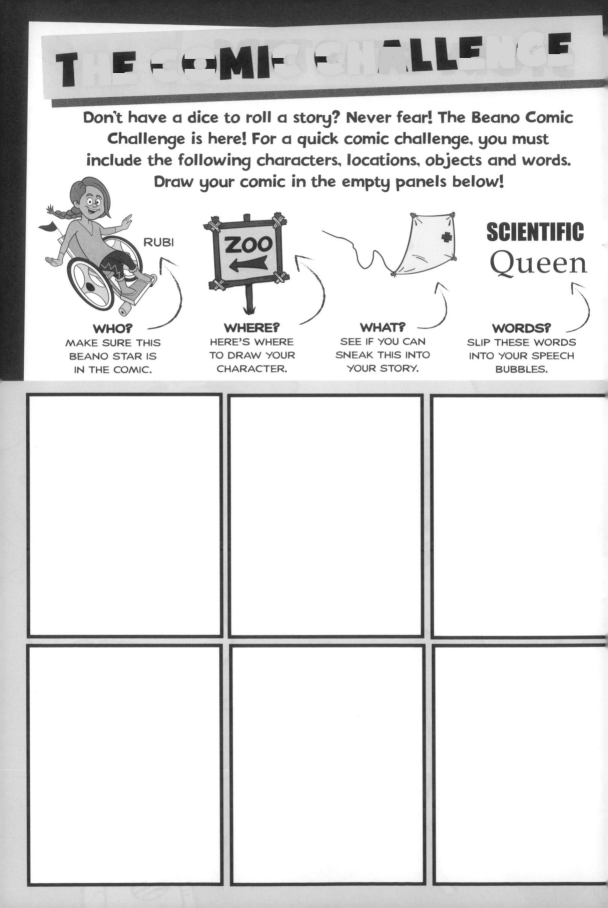

RUBI

ZOO

SCIENTIFIC Queen

WHO?
MAKE SURE THIS BEANO STAR IS IN THE COMIC.

WHERE?
HERE'S WHERE TO DRAW YOUR CHARACTER.

WHAT?
SEE IF YOU CAN SNEAK THIS INTO YOUR STORY.

WORDS?
SLIP THESE WORDS INTO YOUR SPEECH BUBBLES.

STORY STARTERS

A good way to come up with a story idea, is to think of a 'What If'. There are some Beanotown 'What Ifs' below – add your own and then choose your favourites to turn into a comic strip!

WHAT IF . . .

WHAT IF BEANOTOWN RAN OUT OF ICE CREAM?

WHAT IF . . .

WHAT IF DINOSAURS TOOK OVER BEANOTOWN?

WHAT IF THERE WAS A CONTAGIOUS BOUT OF THE GIGGLES SPREADING AROUND TOWN?

WHAT IF DENNIS DISCOVERED HIS SKATEBOARD HAD SECRET POWERS?

WHAT IF . . .

PLANNING A
COMIC STRIP

Before you draw your final comic strip, it's a good idea to create a plan of what will happen in each panel. Start by writing down all the scenes you need to show, and then roughly sketch them out. This will help you work out how big each panel needs to be, how big to draw your speech bubbles and if there are any gaps in your story. Have a look at the example, and then turn the page to plan your own strip!

Panel 1:   Dennis wakes up. "Ugh I can't believe I have to go to school today."

Panel 2:   Sleepy Dennis goes downstairs to have breakfast, Mum and Dad aren't there.

Panel 3:   Dennis on skateboard going to school. Postman: "You're up early, Dennis!"

Panel 4:   Dennis decides to play a trick on Walter, so hides in a bush on Walter's route.

Panel 5:   10 minutes later...
"I guess Walter's off sick today." Gnasher shrugs.

Panel 6:   Dennis approaches the school.

Panel 7:   Close-up on Dennis trying to open the door. "Hm, it's locked!"

Panel 8:   Dennis's mum pulls up in the car "DENNIS! What are you doing? It's Saturday!"

Panel 9:   Dennis — face-palms!

Plan your next comic strip using the storyline you created on page 59 (or another awesome story you've thought of!). Remember to write down what's going to happen in each panel in the notes below, and then roughly sketch the action into the panels opposite.

Panel 1:

Panel 2:

Panel 3:

Panel 4:

Panel 5:

Panel 6:

Panel 7:

Panel 8:

Panel 9:

CREATE YOUR OWN
COMIC BOOK

The time has come to put everything you've learnt into action. The next few pages have empty comic strips, ready for you to fill with your hilarious storylines and characters.

On pages 76–87 you will find blank story sheets and plotting pages. Use these to plan your storylines and panels. At the back of the book you will also find more characters and props for you to copy and use in your storylines.

Design your front cover on the opposite page, and then use the panels to create your very own comic strips!

DRAW YOUR COMIC BOOK COVER

Look back at the top tips on page 56 and create a cover for your very own comic book! You might find it easier to complete this after you've written each strip as you can choose your favourite storyline and scene to show on the cover.

MAKE SURE YOUR FRONT COVER IS AS BRIGHT AND AS COLOURFUL AS ME!

GNASH GNASH GNICE COVER!

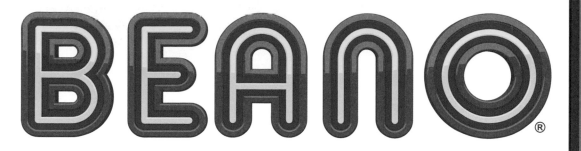

CREATE YOUR OWN

Fill these pages with your funniest comic strips.

COMIC STRIPS

THAT'S SO FUNNY!

IT'S TIME FOR ERIC TO EAT A BANANA!

72

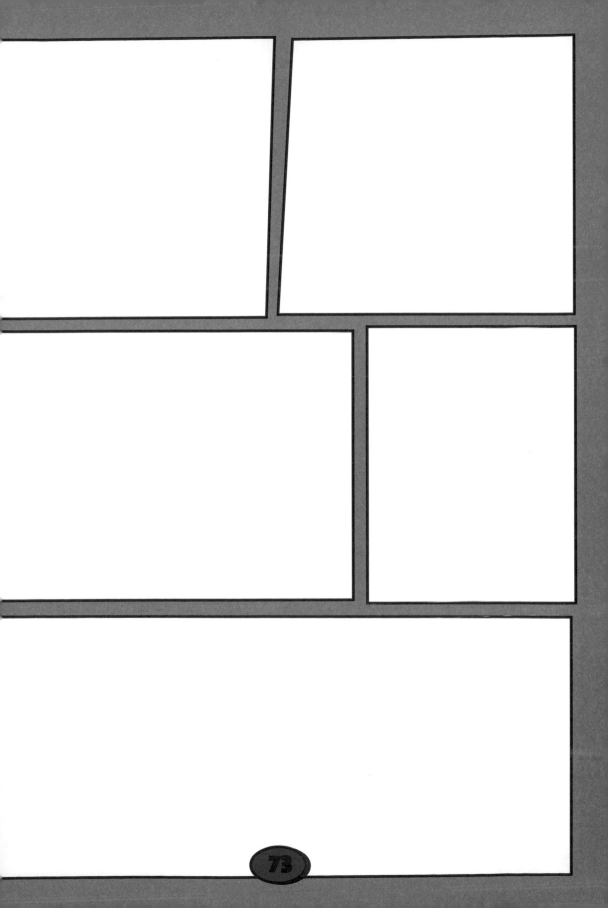

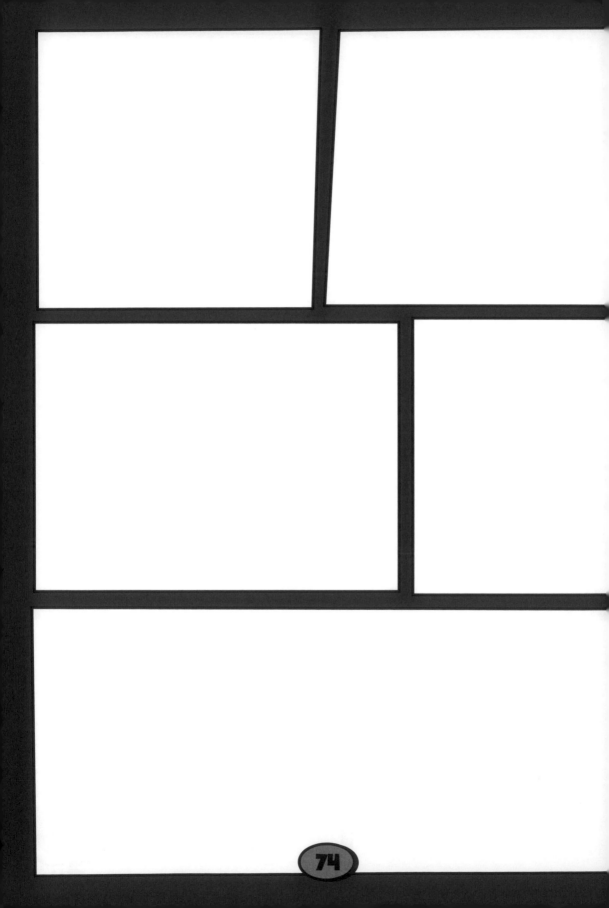

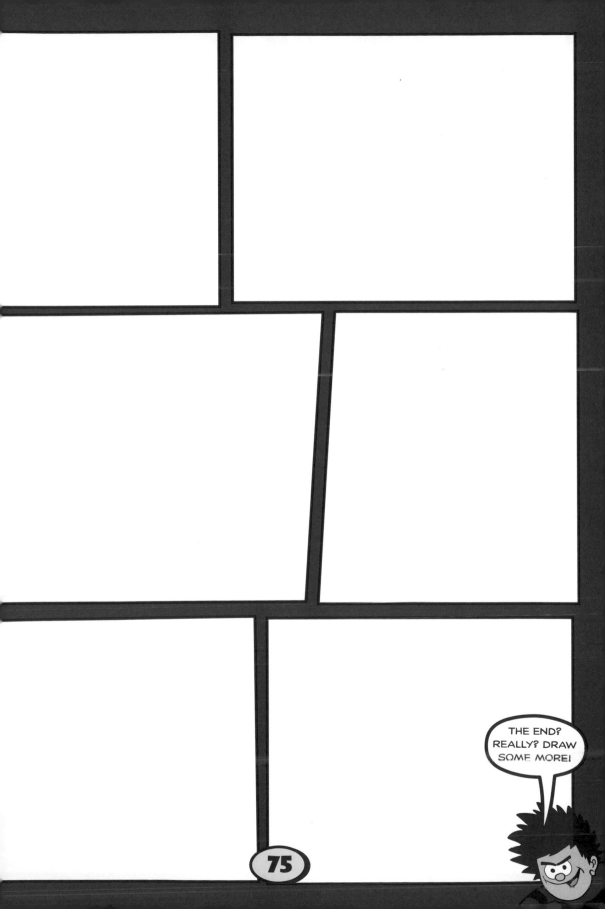

THE END? REALLY? DRAW SOME MORE!

BLANK STORY SHEETS

This section is filled with resources to help you create more and more comic strips. Here are some blank story sheets – fill these in, or make a copy so you can come up with even more storylines!

TITLE

BEGINNING

WHO IS THE MAIN CHARACTER IN THE STORY? --------------------------------------

WHAT DOES THE CHARACTER WANT OR NEED? --------------------------------------

----

WHERE IS THE STORY SET? --------------------------------------

MIDDLE

WHAT PROBLEM DOES YOUR CHARACTER COME UP AGAINST? ----------------------

----

HOW DOES YOUR CHARACTER REACT TO THE PROBLEM? -------------------------

----

HOW DOES THE CHARACTER FEEL? --------------------------------------

----

WHAT'S THE MAIN ACTION? --------------------------------------

----

END

HOW IS THE PROBLEM SOLVED? --------------------------------------

----

HOW DOES YOUR CHARACTER FEEL? -----------------------------------

THIS STORYLINE
IS AWESOME!

TITLE

BEGINNING

WHO IS THE MAIN CHARACTER IN THE STORY? -----------------------------------

WHAT DOES THE CHARACTER WANT OR NEED? ------------------------------------

----

WHERE IS THE STORY SET? --

MIDDLE

WHAT PROBLEM DOES YOUR CHARACTER COME UP AGAINST? --------------------------

----

HOW DOES YOUR CHARACTER REACT TO THE PROBLEM? -----------------------------

----

HOW DOES THE CHARACTER FEEL? ---

WHAT'S THE MAIN ACTION? --

END

HOW IS THE PROBLEM SOLVED? ---

HOW DOES YOUR CHARACTER FEEL? --

TITLE

BEGINNING

WHO IS THE MAIN CHARACTER IN THE STORY? -------------------------------------

WHAT DOES THE CHARACTER WANT OR NEED? --------------------------------------

----

WHERE IS THE STORY SET? --

MIDDLE

WHAT PROBLEM DOES YOUR CHARACTER COME UP AGAINST? ------------------------

----

HOW DOES YOUR CHARACTER REACT TO THE PROBLEM? ---------------------------

----

HOW DOES THE CHARACTER FEEL? --

WHAT'S THE MAIN ACTION? ---

END

HOW IS THE PROBLEM SOLVED? --

HOW DOES YOUR CHARACTER FEEL? ---

TITLE

....

BEGINNING

WHO IS THE MAIN CHARACTER IN THE STORY? -------------------------------

WHAT DOES THE CHARACTER WANT OR NEED? --------------------------------

....

WHERE IS THE STORY SET? --

....

MIDDLE

WHAT PROBLEM DOES YOUR CHARACTER COME UP AGAINST? --------------------

....

....

HOW DOES YOUR CHARACTER REACT TO THE PROBLEM? -----------------------

....

HOW DOES THE CHARACTER FEEL? ---

....

WHAT'S THE MAIN ACTION? --

....

END

HOW IS THE PROBLEM SOLVED? ---

....

....

HOW DOES YOUR CHARACTER FEEL? ---------------------------------------

....

....

WHAT IF ALIENS INVADED?!

BLANK COMIC STRIP PLOTTING SHEETS

Use these blank plotting sheets to plan your comic strips.
Remember to write down what you want to happen in
each panel and then roughly sketch the action.

Panel 1:

Panel 2:

Panel 3:

Panel 4:

Panel 5:

Panel 6:

Panel 7:

Panel 8:

Panel 9:

WHAT
HAPPENS
NEXT?

Plotting sheet

Panel 1:

Panel 2:

Panel 3:

Panel 4:

Panel 5:

Panel 6:

Panel 7:

Panel 8:

Panel 9:

WRITE ME INTO YOUR STORY!

Plotting sheet

GNASH GNASH GNICE STORY!

Panel 1:

Panel 2:

Panel 3:

Panel 4:

Panel 5:

Panel 6:

Panel 7:

Panel 8:

Panel 9:

Plotting sheet

Panel 1:

Panel 2:

Panel 3:

Panel 4:

Panel 5:

Panel 6:

Panel 7:

Panel 8:

Panel 9:

CHARACTERS TO COPY

Beano is filled with amazing characters. Be inspired by your favourites and copy these poses into your own comic strips.

RUBI

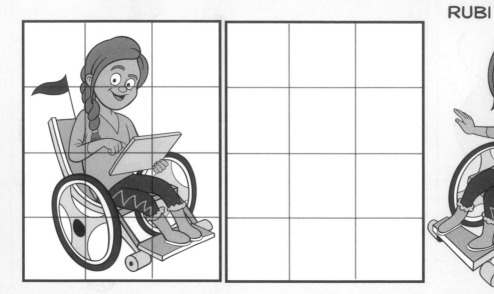

DENNIS'S MUM & DAD

TRICKY DICKY

SERGEANT SLIPPER

CALAMITY JAMES

DR GLOOM

ANGEL FACE

BILLY WHIZZ

WALTER

THE BASH STREET PUPS

BANANAMAN

BEA

BEANO CHARACTER FACES

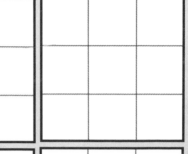

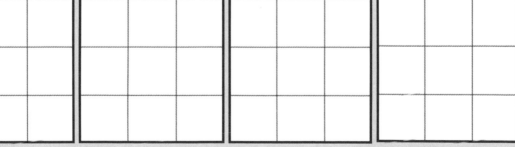

EXTRA PROPS

MORE BEANO FUN...